The Regional In\

Pub Interiors of S

East Anglia's True Heritage Pubs

CAMRA's pioneering initiative for bringing greater recognition and protection to East Anglia's most priceless historic pubs

Edited by Paul Ainsworth

Contents

ACKNOWLEDGEMENTS
The editor would like to thank those members of CAMRA Branches in East Anglia, local planning authorities and interested individuals who contributed suggestions and information to make this booklet possible. Gratitude also to Geoff Brandwood and Mick Slaughter for reading the text and making suggestions for its improvement. In addition, the editor appreciates the support for the project from CAMRA's Pub Campaigns Committee and National Executive and their deep commitment to the Campaign's historic pubs initiatives.

Introduction

East Anglia as defined in this guide – Bedfordshire, Cambridgeshire, Essex, Hertfordshire, Norfolk and Suffolk – has some 6000 public houses. The Regional Inventory lists those with interiors of significant historic or architectural importance – a mere 90 pubs, or less than 2%.

Why is the list so short? One reason, of course, is that pub interiors have always been subject to change. The only pubs which look now as they did the day they opened are those which came into being in the last few years. However, the pace of change has quickened. Most of our few remaining historic interiors evolved slowly over time and clung on to their most endearing features. Recent times have seen a mania for opening out, theming, image change and general trashing that has seen many a pub suffer regular radical makeovers during which most, if not all, vestiges of original or early features have disappeared.

An irony here is that interest in historic buildings has probably never been higher. Lots of us are fascinated by our built heritage and spend many an hour visiting old properties from stately homes through to the most vernacular of structures. This broadening of interest is reflected in recent National Trust openings like the Back to Backs in Birmingham and Mr Straw's House in Worksop. All the more strange, then, that genuine pub interiors seem so undervalued and owners so keen to rip them apart.

The National Inventory

Defending our traditional pubs has always been a key aim of CAMRA. Work began in 1991 to compile a National Inventory of Pub Interiors of Outstanding Historic Interest. The basic criterion for inclusion was intactness; the interior should remain much as it did before the Second World War (subsequently relaxed to 30 years ago). The most recent edition (July 2003) contained just 205 full entries plus 43 "appendix" entries (pubs which whilst significantly altered contain individual rooms or features of national importance).

left: drinking lobby, Hand and Heart, Peterborough *(Michael Slaughter)*.

3

The National Inventory is an evolving entity. Some pubs have to be dropped because they have closed or been altered; in some cases re-evaluation of an entry has meant that, on reflection, it did not meet the standard (an example in East Anglia being The Butt and Oyster, Pin Mill, Suffolk where further investigation showed that much of what you see now is of relatively recent provenance). On the bright side, even now unspoilt gems are being discovered in rural depths or the back streets of our towns; a good example is the 1930s Hand & Heart in the northern suburbs of Peterborough.

The National Inventory has done much to raise awareness of our rich, if dwindling, heritage of pub architecture. However, its necessarily tight criteria meant that many interiors which retained sufficient of interest to be regarded as of regional significance were going formally unrecorded.

Regional Inventories

CAMRA's next step has been to develop a second tier of inventories each covering a region. Here, as with the National Inventory, the focus is on interiors which are authentically old. To be included, a significant amount of genuinely historic internal fabric and/or sufficient of the original layout must be preserved. The emphasis is on pre-1939 interiors though post-war examples of special merit are also admitted. Interiors less than 30 years old, however, do not qualify, CAMRA having chosen to follow the same "30 year rule" that governs statutory listing.

It goes almost without saying that all the relevant National Inventory pubs are included in Regional Inventories, with their status clearly identified.

Regional Inventory descriptions try to make clear the significance of each interior. Other than the National Inventory examples, the pubs fall into two principal categories:

- those with a reasonable degree of intactness in their layout and some of their fittings. Visitors should get a good idea of how the pub was originally arranged even if, for example, doors have been removed or extensions added.

- pubs where the layout has been more radically altered but where particular items or features of real quality survive.

The fact that a pub is not included in the Regional Inventory doesn't mean it has nothing of historic value. The line has to be drawn somewhere so you will come across unlisted pubs with features like etched glass, bar fittings and tilework which are a joy to behold and deserve to be saved.

CAMRA's first Regional Inventory was that for Greater London, published in 2004, and containing 133 pubs. East Anglia is the second and the whole country will, we hope, be covered before very long.

Pubs in East Anglia

A very obvious difference with London is that East Anglia is largely rural. Whilst, therefore, we lack the ornate Victorian treasures in which London is still relatively rich, we do have more than a handful of country pubs which can take you back to a quieter age.

Traditionally, the rural public house was small, if not tiny, and run as a part-time enterprise. Throughout the country, the number of such simple businesses has declined dramatically because they just aren't an economic proposition. Increasingly, rural pubs depend on attracting a car-borne trade which demands food.

Some of our pubs have successfully met this challenge by extending their building in ways which don't impact adversely on their historic core. Good examples are The Cock, Broom,

The Cock, Broom *(Michael Slaughter)*.

Bedfordshire where the additions at the back have been sensitively handled and The Red Lion, Kenninghall, Norfolk, now quite a large establishment, but with the "old bit" still clearly recognisable.

We retain a few diminutive pubs where food offerings go no further than crisps and where fittings are restricted to a handful of tables and chairs. The Rose and Crown at Trowley Bottom and The Rising Sun ("Syds") at High Wych (both Hertfordshire) are classic examples – though how long such pubs can keep going must be open to question.

East Anglia had many coaching inns, many of which survive, albeit in vastly altered form. The Scole Inn, Norfolk is probably the most impressive and, despite what has gone on inside, still gives you a feel of what these places were like. The Crown, Downham Market, West Norfolk and The White Hart, St Ives, Cambridgeshire are other good examples.

Moving into the towns and cities, we have little left from the Victorian and Edwardian eras. The Painters Arms, Luton is certainly the best survivor from these times with its wonderful tiling and tiny snug. A few others, like The Rose and Crown, Bury St Edmunds and The Woolpack, Ipswich, still have their pre-First World War floorplans though most fittings are later.

Arguably our most valuable interiors are those from the inter-war period. Top of the list has to be the remarkable Margaret Catchpole, Ipswich, a wonderful example of the "improved public house". On a smaller scale, The Hand and Heart, Peterborough is an untouched back-street local of 1938; the nearby Greyhound is almost as intact. For Art-Deco fans, The Nags Head, Bishops Stortford isn't to be missed.

Finally, we have our fair share of "picture book" pubs which at first glance look like the genuine article but on examination prove to be partly or largely recent confections. Some, like The Fighting Cocks, St Albans, still have sufficient of interest to merit an entry despite the scale of alterations. Others, such as The Bell, Horndon-on-the-Hill, Essex and The Bell, Stilton, Cambridgeshire, have been so mauled that they must be excluded. There are also quite a few "impressive fakes", pubs which look old but are in fact recent creations, although very well done. The Free Press, Cambridge for instance, was just a shell when the current interior was installed in the 1970s. Similarly, what you see at The Compasses, Littley Green, Essex dates almost entirely to the early 1980s.

ontinuing Review

The entries for this Regional Inventory draw on the accumulated knowledge of CAMRA members throughout the region and we hope to have identified all the interiors worthy of entry. However, with so many pubs across such a big area, there may be historic examples which have escaped our notice – if you find one, do please let us know. Conversely, it's a sad fact that some of the pubs listed will be trashed during the lifetime of this edition – within the couple of years when the Regional Inventory was being compiled, several worthy entries were lost to the hands of the "improvers". The Regional Inventory, like its National counterpart, is an organic document to be kept under constant review and updated in the light of feedback received and our own further research.

ings Head, Laxfield *(Michael Slaughter)*.

The East Anglia Regional Inventory

Broom

23 High Street SG18 9NA

01787 314411

Grade II listed

LPA: Mid Bedfordshire

Cock

A pub which has grown over the years. The room on the left of the entrance is the original public drinking area; drinks were then brought, as they still are, from the cellar behind. Service from the cellar-steps like this was the norm in thousands of pubs in times gone by. The room to the right used to be part of a shop, hence the cupboards either side of the fireplace. The panelling in this room is very fine. The rear part of the pub, with its pretty little snug and public drinking area in front of the cellar entrance, is relatively recent but the expansion has not spoilt the atmosphere of the old front rooms.

BEDFORDSHIRE

Eggington

High Street LU7 0SD

01525 210282

Unlisted

LPA: South Bedfordshire

Horseshoes

The bijou dining room and the upstairs gallery are recent additions though the latter is certainly characterful. The two main bars do, however, survive intact along with some period fixtures and fittings like the fireplace, stove and panelling. Floors are part-tiled, part-boarded. The trendy décor, with lots of dark red, won't be to everyone's taste but it will not leave a permanent mark.

BEDFORDSHIRE

Luton

63 Bute Street LU1 2EY

01582 729311

Unlisted

LPA: Luton

Great Northern

The term "little gem" has become something of a cliché but springs immediately to mind on entering this tiny one-bar pub. One door has been blocked out of use but it is otherwise delightfully intact. Green-tiled wainscotting adorns all the walls and the ornate cast iron roof pillar is a notable feature. Some of the patterned glass has been replaced with modern frosted stuff, presumably because of breakages, but all the original glazing bars (some curved) survive. The bar counter is also genuinely old, possibly original.

BEDFORDSHIRE

Luton

79 Hightown Road LU2 0BW

01582 876972

Grade II listed

LPA: Luton

Painters Arms

Built in 1913, this pub is notable for its surviving compartmental plan and its fabulous tiling. A small snug faces the main entrance with seats running down the side and timber and glass screens – this was originally an off-sales area (hence the door saying Jug Bar). The larger bars to the left and right have a fine array of tiling, both in the floors and dadoes. Some opening up and remodeling of the back part took place in 2000 but the impact has been relatively limited.

Champion of the Thames, Cambridge *(Michael Slaughter)*.

Cambridge

68 King Street CB1 1LN
01223 352043
Grade II listed
LPA: Cambridge

Champion of the Thames

One of the few remaining traditional pubs in the city centre, the "Champ" retains, largely unaltered, its late nineteenth-century interior. Both small bars are wood-panelled with (modern) leather upholstered benches and many interesting nooks and crannies. The characterful but frankly disgusting outside loos were replaced several years ago by more civilized indoor arrangements. The etched windows, showing the Champion in action, are marvellous but not original having been smashed and replaced a number of times (the pub lies on the notorious "King Street Run").

Grantchester

57 The Broadway CB3 9NQ
01223 840679
Unlisted
LPA: South Cambridgeshire

Blue Ball Inn

The Blue Ball (whose name commemorates a balloon flight) dates from 1767 but was rebuilt in 1893. The interior plan-form is intact though the internal door has been removed so that the two-bar layout now has more of an open-plan feel. As befits a village local, the fittings are plain and simple but still charming. The increasingly rare traditional pub game of Ring the Bull is played. For a pub this small to have survived in this location is something of a wonder in itself.

Plough and Fleece, Horningsea *(Michael Slaughter)*.

Plough and Fleece

Horningsea

High Street CB5 9JG

01223 860795

Grade II listed

LPA: South Cambridgeshire

A late eighteenth-century or early nineteenth-century building (sales particulars of 1842 describe it as a "brick and tile house recently put in good repair"). The public bar, with its low heavily beamed roof and black-bricked, alcoved fireplace, is truly atmospheric. There has been some remodelling around the bar and the tiled floor is modern but enough remains to warrant an entry. The rest of the building has little or nothing of historic interest.

Chequers

Little Gransden

71 Main Street SG19 3DW

01767 677348

Unlisted

LPA: South Cambridgeshire

Plain three-bar village local. The tiny drinking area inside the front door is the main feature (though beware the landlord's secret weapon if you linger long in here!). To the right is a basic drinking room. The room to the left is recent but has been sympathetically done. Pubs as uncomplicated as this are becoming increasingly difficult to find.

Queens Head, Newton *(Michael Slaughter)*.

CAMBRIDGESHIRE

Queens Head

Newton

Fowlmere Road CB2 5PG
01223 870436
Grade II listed
LPA: South Cambridgeshire

A pub since at least 1729 though the building is older. The achingly traditional public bar has many original fixtures and fittings, including a splendid high-backed settle. The lounge was significantly extended in the 1950s with the toilets and games annexe being added as late as 1963 but all the work is very much in sympathy with the historic core. The beer is still served from casks stillaged behind the bar.

CAMBRIDGESHIRE ☆

Hand and Heart

Peterborough

12 Highbury Street PE1 3BE
01733 564653
Unlisted
LPA: Peterborough

Back street local unspoilt since its construction in 1936. A corridor runs down the left of the pub and has a small drinking lobby with a hatch to the servery. The public bar is as plain and simple as a public bar should be whilst the lounge/smoke room at the back is almost as no-nonsense (though like the public it suffers from a new fireplace) and has a hatch to the back of the bar. Most of the original Warwick's Brewery windows remain.

**Dogsthorpe,
Peterborough**
Welland Road PE1 3RZ
01733 554890
Grade I listed
LPA: Peterborough

Blue Bell

Originally a farmhouse, it has a datestone of 1669 but has been a pub since 1808. The public bar has been comprehensively remodelled whilst the lounge occupies a 1923 extension built in the style of the old building. This incorporates some fragments of old panelling found during the alterations. A wood-panelled corridor leads to a snug where the panelling is very fine indeed; there is also a huge inglenook with a massive beam, sadly despoiled by insertion of a modern fireplace. The panelling has a date on it of 1594 so must have been brought from elsewhere at some stage.

Peterborough
613 Lincoln Road PE1 3HA
Ex Directory
Unlisted
LPA: Peterborough

Greyhound

Built in 1937 and retaining its original floor plan. A recent refurbishment has been carried out very sensitively. To the left of the entrance is the public bar with linoleum flooring and what seem to be the original banquette seats and light fittings; the curious circular indentation in the ceiling must once have been a skylight. In the centre is an off-licence servery, closed but still intact. A back corridor leads to the toilets (excellent tiling in the gents') and the simply-appointed, bay-windowed lounge.

Bar, Hand and Heart, Peterborough *(Michael Slaughter)*.

CAMBRIDGESHIRE

St Ives

13 Crown Street PE27 5EB
01480 462586
Grade II listed
LPA: Huntingdonshire

Royal Oak

The 1502 date over the door is spurious as the main part of the building dates from the eighteenth-century and the rear wing is a little older. There have been a number of refurbishments in recent times but the pub retains many separate areas. The front entrance leads into a small front bar with a separate room to the left; the panelling and fireplace here look to be inter-war. A corridor goes through to a large back room with a nice tiled floor but the superb deep fireplaces at each end tell a tale of wall removal. The small back bar with internal windows is a recent creation.

CAMBRIDGESHIRE

St Ives

1 Sheep Market PE27 5AH
01480 463275
Grade II listed
LPA: Huntingdonshire

White Hart

The current building dates from the early eighteenth-century and was a coaching inn (part of the stable block survives at the rear). The central covered passage, now part-tiled and part-flagged, was originally a coaching arch and is the most notable feature here. The bar to the left has some good wall panelling and is essentially intact. The one to the right has been extended backwards and generally knocked about quite recently.

ESSEX

Broad's Green

Great Waltham CM3 1DT
01245 360222
Unlisted
LPA: Uttlesford

Walnut Tree

The front door of this Victorian pub brings you into an unusual snug, squeezed between the two bars. It has little more than two small benches but is delightful nonetheless. A door to the left leads into an exceptional public bar with painted wood-panelling, parquet flooring, padded bench seats and a hatch-style bar counter. The lounge, which has been extended into an adjoining room, is pedestrian by comparison.

ESSEX

Bures Hamlet

1 Station Hill CO8 5DD
01787 228121
Grade II listed
LPA: Colchester

Swan

There has been quite a degree of change here (certainly since 1490 from when the building reputedly dates and more recently since a fire in the 1980s) but the floor plan is largely intact and some decent features remain. The public bar has a very old door and a well-beamed ceiling, with other fittings being early post-war (bench seats and bar counter) or more recent. The lounge also has beams plus some exposed timbers but has been extended into a previously non-pub area to create a dining space. There is also an off-sales, still in use.

ESSEX

Castle Hedingham
10 St James Street CO9 3EJ
01787 460350
Grade II listed
LPA: Uttlesford

Bell

Four rooms linked by a corridor running from the front door. First, on the right, is the public bar which has been rather spoilt by modern half-panelling and an unfortunate fireplace. To the left is a plain room with a few timbers and a glass-fronted section displaying the underlying wattle and daub construction. The corridor then turns 90 degrees and there's a small, well-timbered room on the left and a hatch to the bar on the right. The lounge is at the end. How many of these rooms formed part of the original pub is debatable – probably just the public bar – but the multi-roomed layout is cherishable.

ESSEX   ☆

Mill Green (Ingatestone)
The Common
Mill Green Road CM4 0PT
01277 352010
Unlisted
LPA: Brentwood

Viper

The tap room, with simple fittings, must look just like it did in Victorian times apart from the bright yellow paint and more recent wood-block flooring and fireplace. The hole in the seat and the drawer beneath are for the old pub game of Tossing the Penny. Of the three further rooms, the one on the left seems to have entered pub use in the inter-war period and that on the far right rather later. The separate door to the right hand room was closed up following subsidence in the 1970s, but has recently been brought back into use.

Viper, Mill Green (Ingatestone) Essex *(Michael Slaughter)*.

ESSEX

Pleshey

The Street CM3 1HG
01245 237291
Grade II listed
LPA: Uttlesford

Leather Bottle

The public bar has bags of atmosphere though it was clearly two rooms at one point. It has painted wood-panelling on walls and ceiling (brown and cream – the best colour scheme for pubs!), bench seating, brick fireplace and a part-tiled and part-woodblock floor. Shame about the opening which has been created next to the bar counter into the lounge (which is small but unremarkable).

ESSEX

Southminster

Burnham Road CM0 7BL
01621 772915
Unlisted
LPA: Maldon

Rose Inn

Both rooms in this small two-bar pub have been extended somewhat, to their detriment, although the door between them has been reinstated recently and includes the former serving hatch. However, the brick wall and fireplace separating the bars is most attractive. The public bar is pleasingly simple, with bench seating. The lounge is disfigured with 4 × 2 "beams" but these could easily be removed.

ESSEX

South Weald, Brentwood

Weald Road CM14 5QJ
01277 210266
Grade II listed   LPA: Brentwood

Tower Arms

This Georgian-style former shooting lodge has been a pub since 1921. There are three rooms, opulently panelled and presumably little altered from the previous incarnation. A conservatory-style extension has been sensitively handled.

ESSEX

Walton-on-the-Naze

3 Old Pier Street CO14 8AN
01255 674000
Grade II listed
LPA: Tendring

Royal Marine

The high-ceilinged, part-panelled lounge bar is very much the star here. The large, leaded, frosted-glass windows continue at right angles internally to form an unusual part division with the public bar; this has been extended by opening out into a previously separate back room. A doorless space leads from this into what is now used as a restaurant area but which retains a carved bar counter and painted panelling. Must have once been wonderful but still pretty good.

HERTFORDSHIRE

Aldbury

19 Stocks Road HP23 5RT
01442 851228
Unlisted
LPA: Dacorum

Greyhound Inn

"Untouched by Progress" proclaims the little public bar and the claim is well supported by the original fireplace, wainscotting and bar counter, all of which contribute to a simple but satisfying whole. The other bar has been greatly enlarged and opens onto several dining areas which have accumulated to the rear.

HERTFORDSHIRE

Ayot St Lawrence
Bride Hall Lane AL6 9BT
01438 820250
Grade II listed
LPA: Welwyn Hatfield

Brocket Arms

As long ago as 1963 this old pub was being referred to as "a good deal restored". Even so, it merits an entry for its two atmospheric, low-ceilinged rooms, both adorned with a plethora of fine beams and one graced with a splendid inglenook fireplace. Parts of the building date from the fifteenth-century though the first reference to it as licensed is 1694. The king post roof is notable.

HERTFORDSHIRE

Benington
4 Town Lane SG2 7LA
01438 869270
Grade II* listed
LPA: East Herts

Bell

A seventeenth century building (though the pub's own blurb claims earlier), this was recorded as an alehouse in 1693 and was restored around 1850. The large wall painting in the main bar, depicting a stag hunt and dating to circa 1720, really is a wonder to behold – and the fireplace below it is also impressive. The rest of this room has been slightly extended and has a recent bar counter but is otherwise unspoilt. The other room has a nice old boarded floor but has seen more radical enlargement.

HERTFORDSHIRE

Bishops Stortford
216 Dunmow Road CM23 5HP
01279 654553
Grade II listed
LPA: East Herts

Nag's Head

1934 art deco pub by E B Musman who also designed the now internally ruined Comet at Hatfield. The public bar is remarkably intact, retaining its L-shaped layout, bar fittings, windowsills which bulge out to form tables, marble-slab fireplace and doors. The corridor leading to the lounge has post-hole windows (the pub was designed to resemble a ship). The present lounge was formerly two rooms – a saloon bar with private bar behind. The bar counter and bar back survive though, as does the fireplace. Sensitively renovated recently by its new owners.

HERTFORDSHIRE

Bridens Camp
HP2 6EY
01442 253250
Unlisted
LPA: Dacorum

Crown and Sceptre

The three low-ceilinged rooms here each have plenty of character. To the left of the entrance is a small room with a wood-surround fireplace, a carved settle and bench seating. On the right is another small room which has half-panelling, quarry-tiled flooring near the bar and a brick fireplace. Best room of the three is the tiny one at the back – oak panelling on two walls, a hatch/half doorway to the bar, a good fireplace and bare wooden floor.

17

HERTFORDSHIRE

Bushey
25 Park Road WD23 3EE
020 8950 2256
Unlisted
LPA: Hertsmere

Swan
A treasurable example of a relatively unspoilt Victorian back-street local (first reference to it is as a beer house in 1866), The Swan is unusually located within a terrace. The former Jug and Bottle has been incorporated into the public space, though the door (with neat etching) remains; there were also evidently two rooms at one time and the dartboard resides in a later backwards extension. A lot of the fittings – bar counter, doors, windows, wall-panelling – are, if not original, then very old.

HERTFORDSHIRE

Harpenden
39 High Street AL5 2SD
01582 763989
Grade II listed
LPA: St Albans

Cross Keys
This two-bar town pub dates back to at least 1731 (when it was The White Hart). It had a make-over in the 1950s and it is that largely intact design scheme which now generates interest. Various "olde worlde" features were incorporated such as brick fireplaces with medieval overtones, leaded windows, bench seats and a pewter bar top – the fine stone-flagged floor and oak beams are probably much older. The public bar has more character than the lounge.

HERTFORDSHIRE

Hertford
31–33 Castle Street SG14 1HH
01992 501950
Grade II listed
LPA: East Herts

White Horse
Probably a seventeenth century building, this was a pub by 1838. Until the late 1970s it was a single bar enterprise, the original being the left hand one (and largely unaltered apart from the openings to the "new" areas). The right hand bar is an opening-up into the former residential space whilst the incorporation of parts of the upper floor into the public area is quite recent.

HERTFORDSHIRE

High Wych
High Wych Road (B1184)
CM21 0HZ
01279 724099
Unlisted   LPA: East Herts

Rising Sun
Known locally as "Sid's", this pub has three rooms of unspoilt, classic simplicity; the separate room to the right of the entrance is a special delight. Some might feel that from an architectural standpoint there is nothing at all remarkable here but it's the very straightforwardness of the interior which is so cherishable (and rare).

HERTFORDSHIRE

Hitchin
31 Walsworth Street SG4 9ST
01462 432615
Unlisted   LPA: North Herts

Radcliffe Arms
The wood-panelled lounge is a splendidly intact example of 1930s décor and styling. The bar counter appears original and has a complete set of four rolling wooden shutters as well as an untampered-with bar back. There are latticed, leaded windows at the front and leaded French windows

at the back. An alcove opposite the bar accommodates a wood-surrounded fireplace with a coat of arms painted above. An archway two-thirds the way down the room creates a separate area near the French windows. The external and toilet doors have leaded, stained-glass windows. The basic public bar has little of interest thought the bench seating may be original.

HERTFORDSHIRE

Newgate Street

51 Newgate Street Village
SG13 8RA
01707 873236
Grade II listed
LPA: Welwyn Hatfield

Coach and Horses

The original four-room layout has suffered from a fair degree of opening out though the floor-plan is still clearly discernible and plenty of old timbering and panelling remains. The stone-flagged floor in the main bar also has an authentic look. The extension into a former stables/outbuilding has been sensitively accomplished.

HERTFORDSHIRE

Radlett

18 Cobden Hill WD7 7JR
01923 469523
Grade II listed
LPA: Hertsmere

Cat and Fiddle

An early nineteenth-century building, this was first recorded as a pub in 1845. There are currently three rooms, linked by having had the doors removed, but there would have been more rooms originally. Interesting features include lots of oak panelling, carved settles (including a fine high-backed example) and some nice benching. There are jarring elements too, though, notably a brutish modern fireplace and nasty bright padded benches in one room.

HERTFORDSHIRE

Reed

High Street SG8 8AH
01763 848366
Grade II listed
LPA: North Herts

Cabinet

Weatherboarded village pub and restaurant, with the emphasis now more on the latter. The main bar has an old tiled floor and an inglenook fireplace; what was once a serving hatch has been much extended. The side room has a good brick floor and, like the back room, is simply appointed – pity that the opening between the bar and the back room has been so much widened. The restaurant/dining room behind the bar is recent, tasteful and of no interest.

HERTFORDSHIRE

St Albans

35 Lower Dagnall Street AL3 4PT
01767 851025
Unlisted
LPA: St Albans

Farriers Arms

This has been a pub since at least 1869; part of the building was originally a shop which was incorporated into the pub early last century. Today's interior is a rare, complete design scheme from the early 1960s; it even features a sliding door between the two bars. Grained, light-wood panelling is abundant and there is much "period" furniture, including unusual padded stools. The lower bar has lino-tiled flooring, as does part of the upper.

HERTFORDSHIRE

St Albans

16 Abbey Mill Lane AL3 4HE
01767 865830
Grade II listed
LPA: St Albans

Fighting Cocks

A pub with a much-disputed history; it may or may not have originated as a sixteenth-century dovecote. What is certain is that it has been much altered and opened out over the last forty years, though the positions of most of the former small rooms can still be discerned. The octagonal section known as the cockpit is at a lower level than the rest of the pub and is the most notable feature. Some of the heavy low beams and the inglenook are the real thing but there is also a good deal of fakery here.

Fighting Cocks, St Albans *(Michael Slaughter)*.

HERTFORDSHIRE

St Albans
34–36 Fishpool Street AL3 4RX
01727 855669
Grade II listed
LPA: St Albans

Lower Red Lion

A sixteenth-century former coaching inn with two bars. The Ver Bar has some very fine panelling and an imposing fireplace (though the back wall with its exposed brick strikes a discordant note). The Albion Bar displays evidence of opening out but retains some good beams and another superior fireplace.

HERTFORDSHIRE

Stocking Pelham
SG9 0HZ
01279 777217
Grade II listed
LPA: East Herts

Cock

A pub by 1837, this weatherboarded and thatched building probably dates back to the previous century. The front bar, back bar and what seems to have been an outbuilding have been opening up into one space. The "outbuilding" has an amazing rough-cast semi-circular roof with protruding timbers. The rest is very heavily beamed and timbered. This must have once been an outstanding pub and enough survives to merit an entry.

HERTFORDSHIRE

Trowley Bottom (Flamstead)
AL3 8DP
Ex Directory
Grade II listed
LPA: Dacorum

Rose and Crown

The sheer minuteness of this pub makes it a significant survivor. There is a small public and a minuscule lounge – the door between them has been removed but the opening has not been enlarged. The copious veneered panelling is probably the same vintage as the brick fireplace (1950s). However, it's not the fittings but the scale and the simplicity of the place which makes it really special. The pub only opens in the evenings (from 8pm).

NORFOLK

Blickling
NR11 6NF
01263 732133
Grade II listed
LPA: Broadland

Buckinghamshire Arms

Built in 1693 and part of the Blickling Hall estate. The snug, tucked between the main corridor and the lounge, really is the star here; it's simply furnished and has an unusually shaped alcove. The lounge is also a room of distinction albeit on an altogether more sophisticated plane. The part-tiled corridor and entrance lobby are worthy of note as well. The dining room was only brought into pub use fairly recently.

NORFOLK

Brancaster Staithe
Main Road PE31 8BJ
01485 210314
Unlisted
LPA: West Norfolk

Jolly Sailors

Although the internal doors have been removed, the original three-room layout is largely intact. On the fixtures and fittings front, the tiled floors and rustic brick fireplaces are good, but the recent wainscotting and bar counter somewhat regrettable. The restaurant extension to the rear doesn't impinge significantly. Outside Gents!

21

Lord Nelson, Burnham Thorpe *(Michael Slaughter)*.

Burnham Thorpe

Walsingham Road PE31 8HL
01328 738241
Grade II listed
LPA: West Norfolk

Lord Nelson

The recent renovations have done little to diminish the charms of this glorious pub, though the degree of expansion around the historic core sadly disqualifies it from the National Inventory. The central room with its flagstone, high settles and bar-less servery is truly terrific and must look much as it did in Victorian times although a small bar counter was added in 2003 (before that, drinks were brought to your table); the dining room to the right is a recent creation but has been skilfully done. The great admiral after whom the pub is named was born in the village.

aister
Manor Road NR30 5HG
1493 722426
Unlisted
PA: Great Yarmouth

Never Turn Back

Two bars in a remarkable Odeon-style beach-front extravaganza built by Lacons of Yarmouth. The main entrance is in a square two-storey tower adorned with curious panels inlaid with abstract patterns of flint, brick and stone. To one side is a tall, slim, oval sub-tower with the Lacon's falcon perched on top. The single storey flat roof bars are right and left, each with a veranda supported by brick pillars. Fittings in both bars seem largely intact – panelling, doors, benches and ornate bar counters (the one in the public being especially fine with brick and pebble inlays).

Clenchwarton
243 Main Road PE34 4AQ
01553 660682
Unlisted
PA: West Norfolk

Victory Inn

Apart from the recent addition of indoor toilets, there have been no significant changes to this pub since 1962. The public bar sports upholstered bench seats, Formica-topped tables, lino-tiled floor, tiled fireplaces and a padded leather bar front. The lounge has carpet, tiled fireplace, juke box and leatherette benches, the last being especially delectable. The off-sales window in the entrance hall is also intact.

Costessey
79 Norwich Road
New Costessey NR5 0EU
01603 742849
Unlisted   LPA: Norwich

Crown

The lounge in this inter-war suburban pub has been refurbished into anonymity. However the public is pleasantly basic and little altered, with a plain, sturdy bar counter, painted bar back and shelving plus some interesting moulding on the walls. The widened opening to the games room doesn't detract over-much.

Downham Market
12 Bridge Street PE38 9DW
01366 382322
Grade II listed
LPA: West Norfolk

Crown Hotel

The interior of this seventeenth-century coaching inn has been subjected to much change over the years but it retains considerable interest and atmosphere. The wall panelling (rescued from Didlington Hall prior to its demolition) and the large fireplace in the main bar are undeniably ancient but the bar counter is a horrid modern imposition. The jettied area at the back is also worthy of note.

Gaywood
9 Wootton Road PE30 4EZ
01553 763258
Unlisted
LPA: West Norfolk

White Horse

A Victorian building with a 1960s extension, from when much of the interior décor appears to date. The public bar has a Formica-topped bar and unusual patterned-glass windows. The lounge has stripped pine wainscoting and bar counter but the sliding door was recently removed. The loos are splendidly unmodernised. Not to everybody's taste, but a survivor nevertheless.

NORFOLK

Hethersett

36 Old Norwich Road NR9 3DD
01603 810206
Grade II listed
LPA: South Norfolk

Kings Head

Worth visiting for the absolute gem of a snug. It has a separate entrance, an old tiled floor, a brick fireplace and original-looking fittings. Nothing fancy but one of those rooms which achieves its own kind of perfection. It was also the scene of the arrest of a local murderer in 1817 – details of the event are displayed on the wall. The rest of the pub, though heavily-beamed, has been comprehensively remodelled and extended.

NORFOLK

Heydon

The Street NR11 6AD
01263 587376
Grade II listed
LPA: Broadland

Earle Arms

The lounge and public bar are either side of an entrance lobby with a modern dining room and conservatory further back. Apart from a choice fireplace, the lounge is of no interest. The public bar, though, is delightfully rustic with a hatch-style bar counter, moulded fireplace, curious cupboards and big beams. The pine wainscotting is recent but a segment of original panelling under the window gives an idea of how things once were. The alcove apparently used to house a staircase to a long-gone club room.

NORFOLK

Hilborough

Swaffham Road IP26 5BW
01760 756380
Grade II listed
LPA: Breckland

Swan

The main bar area here is lovely, with polished wood floor and a gorgeous bar counter, panelled and moulded. The brick fireplace is a disappointment, though the original apparently lurks behind it. The lounge area is very dull and the arched recesses are especially naff. A stone-flagged corridor leads to the back room which contains some good timbering as well as an original and recently uncovered fireplace.

NORFOLK

Kenninghall

East Church Street NR16 2EP
01953 887849
Grade II listed
LPA: South Norfolk

Red Lion

The original buildings are believed to be 400 years old; the pub had, however, been shut for seven years before being reopened in 1997 after major refurbishments. The crowning glory is the snug to the right of the entrance which clearly started as a big settle, then had boarding extended to the ceiling and side. The main bar has been much altered but retains a rustic beam over both the fireplace and a former oven. The corridor has original tiling and leads to a large dining room (not part of the original pub) with tiled floor, alcoves and large fireplace.

Red Lion, Kenninghall *(Michael Slaughter)*.

NORFOLK

Neatishead

The Street NR12 8AD
01692 630828
Unlisted
LPA: North Norfolk

White Horse Inn

Village local, reputedly built in 1815 though the front part dates from later that century. Of the two main bars, the lower one at the rear is the better, having a tiled floor and impressive black-leaded range. The upper room has a hatch-style bar counter, a (blocked) fireplace and bench seating – replacement "leaded" PVC windows strike a jarring note. The dining room to the left of the entrance has only recently been brought into pub use. The barn and other outbuildings to the rear are also noteworthy.

NORFOLK

Norwich

17 Bishopsgate NR3 1RZ
01603 667423
Grade II listed
LPA: Norwich

Adam and Eve

Self-proclaimed as the oldest pub in Norwich, parts of the fabric are indubitably ancient (13th to 15th centuries) though the interior has been knocked around a lot in recent times. Of the two bars at ground level, the one describing itself as a snug is of 1930s vintage and has good panelling and tiling. Most of the remainder dates back only to the early 1970s, which is when the lower bar (formerly the cellar, from which there was jug service) was brought into use. Fittings generally are a mixture of old and repro but there's some authentically interesting stuff here. The building apparently originated as a brewhouse associated with the nearby Cathedral.

NORFOLK

Norwich

174 Ber Street NR1 3EN
01603 620623
Unlisted
LPA: Norwich

Berstrete Gates

Of the three rooms the one currently used for pool is the best, being small, oak-panelled and little altered from the 1930s (from when the overall décor seems to date). The main bar also sports some pleasant panelling and leaded windows but has been enlarged by incorporation of a lobby area. A third room has panelling of more recent vintage and is unlikely to have formed part of the original pub. The wall sign is a mural by Moray Smith depicting one of the city gates.

NORFOLK

Norwich

Dereham Road NR5 8QJ
01603 620340
Unlisted
LPA: Norwich

Gate House

Mock Tudor/Baronial-style affair dating from 1934. The two bars retain their original panelling and moulded dados. The lounge still has a serving hatch rather than a bar counter. The public bar has been knocked through into what had been a separate room and which has a superb curved window. The half-timbering in the ceiling is very odd! A new porch has been added but is in keeping with the rest (not so the tacky conservatory). The exterior is also most distinctive.

Norwich
36 Market Street NR2 1RD
01603 615892
Grade II listed
LPA: Norwich

Sir Garnet Wolsey

A pub since 1886 (it was previously a butcher's shop), it has two bars on two levels. The lower one is narrow, dominated by a newish bar counter, with settles along the front wall and some fine old timbers. The top bar is quieter with painted panelling over what were recently bare brick walls plus exposed beams. Despite its small size it is rumoured that two other pubs (The Half Moon and The Punch Bowl) were incorporated into it at one stage.

Norwich
Browne Street NR2 4QY
01603 626490
Unlisted
LPA: Norwich

West End Retreat

One of those pubs whose very ordinariness and simplicity impart a charm all of their own. The building is early twentieth century but most of what we now see dates from the1950s/1960s; none of the fixtures and fittings is especially remarkable but few interiors of this vintage haven't had at least one makeover since then. Two bars, an off-sales and some old Bullards windows. Also has a bowling green at the back.

Scole
Ipswich Road IP21 4DR
01379 740481
Grade I listed
LPA: South Norfolk

Scole Inn

Imposing grade I-listed coaching inn (built by John Peck in 1655) with a magnificent situation and spectacular inn sign. Inside there's been a fair degree of alteration though both main bars retain their enormous fireplaces, one with a moulded coat of arms above. Beams and external doors are also impressive. The repro bar counter with its "funny" carvings is hideous.

Sheringham
27 Cromer Road NR26 8AB
01263 824825
Unlisted
North Norfolk

Dunstable Arms

Extraordinary 1931-built Tudor-style pub, retaining many original features. The two rooms each have their own entrance with no internal link. The public bar has been combined with an annexe containing a pool table. The front saloon and club room have also been combined; the latter is in "Tudor Hall" style with a high ceiling and exposed timber beams. It also has a magnificent full height chimney breast in brick and tile. Throughout the interior many interesting and sometimes bizarre features survive - brick-arched doorways, timber friezes and benches, original fireplaces and bar counters. The architect's drawings are displayed in the Club Room.

NORFOLK

Snettisham

Old Church Road PE31 7LX
01485 541382
Grade II listed
LPA: West Norfolk

Rose and Crown

Claiming to be of fourteenth-century origin but more likely seventeenth-century at the earliest, the pub has two small rooms, linked at the front by a low opening; both have old fireplaces, tiled floors and exposed beams. A tiled passage leads to an exceptional back room with bare boards, huge fireplace and a neatly panelled (inter-war) bar counter. Major extensions at the back fortunately do not impinge on the historic core.

NORFOLK

Thorpe St Andrew Norwich

148 Plumstead Road East NR7 9NG
01603 702521
Unlisted
LPA: Broadland

Woodside

An enormous inter-war edifice which, thankfully, retains its original plan-form – lounge, public, smoke-room and off-sales (though the last two have been locked out of use recently). Apart from the doors, there isn't much by way of original fittings. As well as the intactness of the layout, the sheer scale of the place makes it noteworthy.

NORFOLK

Walsingham

8 Common Place NR22 6BP
01328 820333
Grade II* listed
LPA: North Norfolk

Bull Inn

The snug back bar looks like a recent creation but the other rooms are much older, albeit not as old as the building (fifteenth-century). A door and part of the wall have been removed between two of the rooms but the impact isn't too drastic. The walls are mildly rough cast with timbers exposed in one area – this is to show charring supposedly caused by pilgrims setting fire to the place in protest at being overcharged. Excellent fireplace in the lounge but most fittings are recent.

NORFOLK

Warham

Bridge Street NR23 1NL
01328 710547
Unlisted
LPA: North Norfolk

Three Horseshoes

The historic core of the pub is essentially intact with little, if any, change from the 1930s. There are three rooms in this portion of which the first, with its screeded floor, half-panelling and scrubbed benches, is the best; note the traditional Norfolk Twister on the ceiling – an early form of Roulette. The second room is also intact apart from the door into a third room, formerly a shop. The metal grilles in the windows of the first room are especially interesting; once common, these are now very rarely found. There have been recent accretions – including a plastic turret-clock! – and the original serving hatch has given way to a bar counter, but it's still a marvellously atmospheric place.

Three Horseshoes, Warham *(Michael Slaughter)*.

NORFOLK

Wymondham
6 Church Street NR18 0PH
01953 607907
Grade II* listed
LPA: South Norfolk

Green Dragon

Parts of the building may date back to the thirteenth-century but generally described as mid fifteenth-century and originally a hostelry to the Benedictine monastery. The room containing the bar is really quite special, dominated by a huge fireplace and oozing character. The cupboard to the left of the fireplace was formerly the site of a winder to a solar whilst, on the right, the stone arched doorway leads to the original exterior. The lounge occupies former shop premises and has little of interest apart from a dragon beam.

SUFFOLK

Beyton
Tostock Road IP30 9AG
01359 270249
Unlisted
LPA: St Edmundsbury

Bear

Built to replace an earlier pub burnt down in 1910, The Bear has a simply appointed lounge and an equally uncomplicated public bar, plus a back room used as a dining room. The lounge has bare floorboards, leatherette benches, Formica-covered bar counter and colour-washed walls. The public has a similar feel, though the floor is tiled. The late 1950s/early 1960s ambience is strong and endearing.

Cock, Brent Eleigh *(Michael Slaughter)*.

Cock

Brent Eleigh
Lavenham Road CO10 9PB
01787 247371
Grade II listed
LPA: Babergh

Attractive thatched pub whose pink rendering conceals a timber frame. The older of the two bars is the one on the right of the front doorway and has wooden panelling in the dado and a bar counter with old woodwork. Note the Tossing the Penny pub game in the bench seating and the shove ha'penny board carved into the large table. The left-hand bar was developed in the 1970s by extending the bar counter into it (service was formerly via a hatch). The off-sales was reduced in scale at the same time.

Number 3

Bury St Edmunds
3 Risbygate Street IP33 3AA
01284 752716
Grade II listed
LPA: St Edmundsbury

Formerly the Market Tavern, this pub is notable for the area to the left of the entrance, which features a quite stunning beamed ceiling plus fine panelling and a good fireplace; you can't help wondering how this room comes to be here. The rest of the place has been subjected to an execrable pseudo-stylish wine-bar refit.

SUFFOLK ☆

Bury St Edmunds

The Traverse IP33 1BJ
01284 705387
Grade II listed
PA: St Edmundsbury

Nutshell

Britain's smallest pub, measuring a mere 4.6m × 2.5. inside. The building is early/mid nineteenth-century and became a beerhouse in 1873. Like many Victorian pubs it contained a collection of curiosities and some are still here, including a mummified cat. The record number of people crammed into the pub is currently 102 (plus a dog).

The Nutshell, Bury St Edmunds
(Michael Slaughter).

31

SUFFOLK

Bury St Edmunds

48 Whiting Street IP33 1NP
01284 755934
Unlisted
LPA: St Edmundsbury

Rose and Crown

This has been a pub since Victorian times but features like the exposed roof beams suggest that the building is older. The original floor plan (two bars plus off-sales) remains. The oddly-shaped public and the cosy lounge both have part-panelled walls and sturdy bar counters. The off-sales unusually has its own set of handpumps.

SUFFOLK

Chelsworth

24/26 The Street IP7 7HU
01449 740758
Grade II listed
LPA: Babergh

Peacock

Parts of the building are reputedly fourteenth-century. Alterations internally have been on quite a major scale but a fair amount of interest remains. The front door leads into a "snug bar" which has some original timbering and a vile semi-circular bar counter. A door leads into the main bar/restaurant, formerly at least two rooms, with plenty of beams and, like the snug, an old brick fireplace.

SUFFOLK

Cockfield

Stows Hill
Lavenham Road IP30 0JB
01284 828177
Grade II listed
LPA: Babergh

Three Horseshoes

The lounge is the thing at this pink-washed, thatched country pub. It has its origins as a fourteenth-century aisled hall, and still sports the original crown post and beams. The public is from a later time but is still itself well above average.

SUFFOLK

Dunwich

St James Street IP17 3DT
01728 648219
Grade II listed
LPA: Suffolk Coastal

Ship

Sturdy Victorian building, though the cellars are from Tudor times. The simple L-shaped bar would once have been two rooms; one half has a lovely tiled floor and an elegant brick fireplace. The wooden benches are old, possibly even original. A dining room and family conservatory lie further back.

SUFFOLK

East Bergholt

Heath Road CO7 6RL
01206 298438
Grade II listed
LPA: Babergh

Hare and Hounds

The spectacular pargetted ceiling (dated from 1590) in one bar is the feature which lifts this otherwise pleasant but much altered pub into the top category. The modern bar counter and fireplaces (complete with coal-effect) are a real let-down. The other bar must have once been at least two or three rooms but there are now only the skeletal remains of former walls.

Hare and Hounds, East Bergholt *(Michael Slaughter)*.

SUFFOLK

Hartest

The Green IP29 4DH
01284 830250
Grade II listed
LPA: Babergh

Crown

The dining room here occupies a fifteenth-century tythe courthouse and has particularly important panelling. The main bar is in a later (eighteenth-century) area; the massive old fireplace, (some) original beams and tiled floor are features of merit but the monolithic bar counter certainly is not. There is also a heavily-beamed back room. Despite a lot of modern accretions like the conservatory and entrance hall, it is still a building of considerable character.

SUFFOLK

Horringer

The Street IP29 5SN
01284 735260
Grade II listed
LPA: St Edmundsbury

Beehive

Originally a flint cottage from the eighteenth-century, the previously multi-room layout is still visible in this pub, though doors have been removed and openings widened. Around the bar is a splendid yellow-tiled floor whilst exposed brick and flint appear in places.

SUFFOLK ☆

Ipswich

Cliff Lane IP3 0PQ
01473 252450
Grade II* listed
LPA: Ipswich

Margaret Catchpole

Built in 1936 by Cobbold and Co., this is a very precious survival of an inter-war improved public house. Inside are three fine rooms – a spacious public bar whose bay window overlooks the bowling green (itself a rarity nowadays), a separate but sizeable lounge and a smaller panelled saloon, which also features a distinctive bar counter curved to fit the shape of the room. Fittings like the panelling, bench seating, bell pushes and parquet flooring are all original. Even the off-sales area survives. Quite remarkable.

Margaret Catchpole, Ipswich
(Michael Slaughter).

Margaret Catchpole, Ipswich *(Michael Slaughter).*

SUFFOLK

Ipswich

1 Tuddenham Road IP24 2SH
01473 253059
Grade II listed
LPA: Ipswich

Woolpack

Occupying what is said to be the oldest brick building in Ipswich, this wonderful pub has four separate rooms. The front snug, with its tongue and groove panelling and wall benches, is the most delightful but the whole place is full of character despite some unsympathetic modern furnishings. The lounge has a fine brick fireplace and painted wainscotting. The games room and public are simply appointed but have few original features. A recent small extension and extensive alterations to the toilets and kitchen areas have, fortunately, not impacted adversely on the historic parts.

SUFFOLK

Ixworth

38 High Street IP31 2HH
01359 230398
Grade II listed
LPA: St Edmundsbury

Pickerel

The building dates back to Tudor times though most of what is visible is Victorian or Edwardian in origin. There has been a good deal of further restoration albeit quite sensitively handled, and a variety of rooms still exist, all leading off a central servery. The pub stable is separately listed as grade II star.

Kings Head, Laxfield *(Michael Slaughter)*.

SUFFOLK

Laxfield

Goram's Mill Lane IP13 8DW

01986 798395

Grade II listed

LPA: Mid Suffolk

Kings Head (Low House)

An undoubted classic. The front doorway of this fifteenth-century building leads into a large room dominated on three sides by high Victorian settles; the backs of these define a corridor running right round the room. To the right is a further room with fixed seating round the walls. Behind this the next room has plain panelling and a large multi-drawered cupboard. Finally you reach the cellar, which has no counter (and all the beer is served by gravity). The dining room in the left hand portion is relatively recent. This is a pub which has to be seen to be believed.

SUFFOLK

Lidgate

The Street CB8 9PP

01638 500275

Grade II listed

LPA: St Edmundsbury

Star Inn

Three drinking areas in this well-beamed 400 year old building, each with a superb fireplace (one with a carved lintel). Old photos in the bar clearly show that extensions into the house next door have taken place at some juncture, but you can't now "see the join". Note the unusual under-bar beer-engines.

SUFFOLK

Orford

uay Street IP12 2NU

1394 450243

rade II listed

PA: Suffolk Coastal

Jolly Sailor

The sea has long deserted the quayside but the authentic nautical atmosphere remains. Steps lead down direct from street level to a simply furnished but superb main bar with low ceiling, flagstone floor and an ancient scrubbed table. To the right is a cracking little snug with its own servery. The dining room to the left has an impressive fireplace but almost certainly represents an extension into an adjoining property. There is a modern portion at the back, thankfully invisible from the old part.

SUFFOLK

in Mill

he Quay IP9 1JW

1473 780764

irade II listed

PA: Babergh

Butt and Oyster

Beautifully situated on the banks of the Orwell, the pub occupies a seventeenth-century building, to which a number of flat roof extensions have been added since the last war. The public bar is especially attractive and has great views of the river; only half of it is original, though, the section with the bar counter occupying one of the extensions. The dining room next door is also part old and part new. Both rooms have fine fireplaces and the bar has some lovely old panelling.

utt and Oyster, Pin Mill *(Michael Slaughter)*.

SUFFOLK

Rumburgh

Mill Road IP19 0NT
01986 785257
Unlisted
LPA: Waveney

Buck

The interior here is a series of rambling interconnected rooms, all with flagstone floors and wood-panelled walls and ceilings. Two original small rooms retain old fittings whilst the other three rooms have come into us more recently. Nonetheless a pub of considerable atmosphere.

SUFFOLK

Shottisham

Hollesley Road IP12 3HD
01394 411617
Grade II listed
LPA: Suffolk Coastal

Sorrel Horse

Probably sixteenth-century in origin but "restored" in 1918 and no doubt again since. We now have two homely and simple bars with beamed ceilings, one with a nice tiled floor, the other with a fine brick fireplace. Worth a listing for the splendidly basic outside Gents' alone, but the pub itself still has considerable merit.

SUFFOLK

Southwold

90 High Street IP18 6DP
01502 722275
Grade II listed
LPA: Suffolk Coastal

Crown Hotel

Included here for the cosy bar at the back of the building and nicknamed "God's Waiting Room". Red leatherette wall benches, half-height wall panelling (probably inter-war) and good (modern) shelving behind the servery all contrast with the upmarket ambience elsewhere in the building.

Crown Hotel, Southwold (Michael Slaughter)

SUFFOLK

Southwold
Back Shore IP18 6TA
01502 722381
Grade II listed
PA: Suffolk Coastal

Harbour Inn

The upper bar here has some of the best vernacular panelling to be seen anywhere – quite remarkable. The lower bar is subject to flooding, so, not surprisingly, has few features of note other than the flagstone floor. The recent development of an adjacent building as a restaurant and the wooden link-throughs don't impact adversely on the older part.

SUFFOLK

Walberswick
Ferry Road/Bell Green IP18 6TN
01502 723109
Grade II listed
PA: Suffolk Coastal

Bell

The two original rooms, over 600 years old, are at the front of the pub but back walls have been removed so that they give directly onto the serving area. Flagstone floors, wooden settles and exposed brickwork feature in both rooms. A large, albeit sympathetic, extension has appeared at the back.

SUFFOLK

Worlingworth
Swan Road IP13 7HZ
01728 628267
Grade II listed
LPA: Mid Suffolk

Swan

Attractive thatched pub with two low-ceilinged, rustically beamed, tiled-floored bars. The wood panelling has been shot-blasted quite recently whereas it would have originally been painted or varnished. The public bar on the left formerly comprised two small rooms and a corridor: it has a protruding fireplace with brick-lined alcoves while the other bar also has a brick fireplace – quite an imposing example for such a small pub.

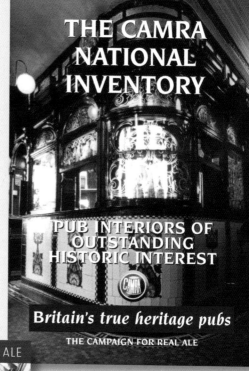